Daily Humor in Russian Life
Ежедневный Юмор в Русской Жизни

Russian caricatures with English translations
Русские карикатуры с английским переводом

Volume 10 - Man's Power
Том 10 - Мужская Сила

Author: Foxy Dime
Автор: Фокси Дайм

First Edition: November 2020

Первое издание: Ноябрь 2020

Volume 10 - Man's Power
Том 10 - Мужская Сила

Author: Foxy Dime
Автор: Фокси Дайм

This book is dedicated to the bright memory of my father, who inspired me to reach higher and never stop learning.

Эта книга посвящена светлой памяти моего отца, который вдохновлял меня достигать большего в жизне и никогда не прекращать учиться.

Introduction

The illustrations in this book were created by my father, who passed away in 2016. I decided to publish this series anonymously, since everything shared in this book, I hold very dear to my heart.

There is stereotype of Russian man, being a protector. Of course, like many of the stereotypes it does not apply to everyone and it is true to certain degree. There is Russian saying «как за каменной спиной» (kak za kame`noy ste`noy) meaning "behind stone wall" that references Russian men in general. My father was exactly that man. He shielded us from the evils of the world and we always feel safe and secure.

Unfortunately, the majority of Russian man love their vodka and cigarettes. According to statistics the average life span of this category of men is 55 years old. Like everywhere in the world, people did not realize danger of smoking until it was too late, including my papa. My papa passed away from lung cancer after battling it for many years.

In Russia military service is mandatory for men of all ages 18 - 27. It used to be two years of service in the past, until it was change to be-12 months a few years back. I do want to mention that my father served in Soviet Army as an officer. Even though his military career was short lived, the service left a lasting impression on my father which reflected in the caricatures.

Another interesting aspect of Russian men is the friendships they develop with other men. These relationships are long lasting whether it is best friend, neighbor, or drinking buddies. This is also reflected in the book.

However, whether you consider yourself woman or man you will have a good laugh reading this book.

Вступление

Иллюстрации в этой книге нарисованы моим отцом, который скончался в 2016 году. Я решила опубликавать эту книгу анонимно, так как содержимое этой книги очень близко и дорого моему сердцу.

Существует стереотип о русском мужчине как о защитнике. Конечно, как и многие стереотипы, это относится не ко всем и только верно до определенной степени. Есть русская поговорка «как за каменной спиной», которая относится к русским мужчинам. Мой отец был именно таким человеком. Он оградил нас от зла этого мира, и мы всегда чувствовали себя в безопасности.

К сожалению, большинство русских мужчин любят водку и сигареты. По статистике, средняя продолжительность жизни этой категории мужчин составляет 55 лет. Как и везде в мире, люди не осознавали опасности курения, пока не стало слишком поздно, включая моего отца. Мой отец скончался от рака легких после многих лет борьбы с этой страшной болезнью.

В России военная служба обязательна для всех мужчин в возрасте от 18 до 27 лет. Раньше это была двухготовая служба, а несколько лет назад закон о службе был изменен, служба теперь составляет на 12 месяцев. Хочу отметить, что мой папа служил в Советской Армии офицером. Несмотря на то, что его военная карьера была недолгой, служба оставила неизгладимое впечатление на моего отца, что нашло отражение в карикатурах.

Ещё один интересный аспект русского мужчины – дружба с друзьями. Эти отношения продолжительны, будь то отношения с лучшими друзьями, соседями или друзьями с повседневной выпивки. Это тоже нашло отражение в этой книге.

Однако независимо от того, считаете ли вы себя мужчиной или женщиной, вы хорошо посмеетесь, прочитав эту книгу.

CARICATURES

КАРИКАТУРЫ

-Only a gentle and tender soul can miss the motherland without leaving it…

-Hey Karla, hold on…

-Who's waving at us and jumping around…?
-I don't know, but he seems joyous every time we swim by.

-Why do I need this receipt?
-If you collect hundreds of them, you can exchange it for a scooter…

-Hey neighbor, can I use your lawn mower?
-Yes, but only within my yard.

-if it's not too difficult for you, can you pass the box with bullets; the enemy is near…!
-What is the magic word?

-Darling, I'm visiting my friend. There is fish for dinner. The fishing rod is by refrigerator.

-If you buy mountain skis, you will get a wheelchair for free...!

-The administration reallocated all of the barbers with bad customer satisfaction records to the garden for bush trimming…

-Is this a separation of belongings or a revolt?

-Given the fact that the dollar exchange rate is falling, $100 is viewed only as verbal gratitude…

-Mirror, mirror tell me the whole truth…

-Prisoner Petrov, come on out; you have visitor…!
-Tell them I'm not here…!

-Young lady, what are you doing on May 5th in the year 2010?

-I don't understand how such a big idiot came into existence from sperm?
-Mama, you know better!

-My wife is worse than "MMM" pyramid scheme. Everything I put into our family, she collected and left to another man...

-Vasyli Ivanovich, how much will 0.5 plus 0.5 be…?
-I feel it will be a liter, but I can't tell scientifically…

-It's hard to call this pile of metal a car…
-That is why I don't have a driver's license…

-Best jumping ever, - pea soup...!

-Would you look at that; he is making fun of us!

-You can't find your stateroom? You didn't memorize the stateroom number?
-No, but I can remember for sure there was a forest in the window.

-Professor, is it true that you're beating your wife?
-That isn't true, I'm not a professor…

-I'm the ghost that has lived in this castle for four hundred years!
-That is awesome; can you tell me, where is the restroom?

-Okay, okay, go to the kitchen... I will buy you your bicycle!

-Land...!
Land...!
-Water...!
Water...!

-Tell me,
how did you
kill this
female bear?
-As always,
-affection,
champaign,
soft music...

-Lieutenant Cidorchok, three children, wife with a sick liver, vacation starting soon…

-I don't believe you…

-Listen, Dog Death, maybe instead of my dog you can take my mother-in-law's cat?

-If you have nothing, why are you roaming at night?

-If you believe the reflection in the paddle, human is a small, slimy and dark being…

-The best way to join nature is to pee in the rain.

-This year men will wear suits without buttons!
-Then it looks like I was dressed fashionably for half of the year…!

-Hello, unknown friend, you can't sleep either?

-It's no fun to be in the top apartment if no one is below you...

-Captain, Land!
-Look forward, we just started sailing...

-Grandpa, I'm not grandma, I'm the wolf! I'm waiting for Red Riding Hood!

Writing on bowls:
"Grand daughter"
"Lover"
"Alimony"
"Wife"
"Debt"
"Medical bills"

-If not for the street signs, I would never have guessed that this is a street…

-What, want some mice? Tired of Whiskas?

Writing on the back “Your advertisement can be here!”

-Defendant, your last word…
-I would like the court to take into consideration my inexperience and the young age of my lawyer!

-Can you please tell me what type of oil should I should pour into the engine?
-Cod-liver oil!

-First, I will pass my college term exams, then I will take the bottles to the recycle station… (In reference to dual meaning of the word “сдать”)

-I won't go scouting with you…!

-You're an idiot…

-Listen Cupid, if you make a hole in the blow-up doll, I will break your arrows!

-You're bolder than I'm, your head is bigger…!

-Nuclear bombs always hit the epicenter of an explosion!

-Soldier, remember! The dark time of the day starts by command “at ease”!

-Comrade ensign, why did the helicopter stop?
-Perhaps he is out of fuel…

-It's better to be idiot than bold. It's not that noticeable to be an idiot…!

-Thank you, and I wish you the same! Thank you and I wish you to get the same! Thank you I wish you would go there too…

-Don’t panic, we are just moving from forward to aft…

-Comrade ensign, if you were not drinking you could have been a lieutenant!
-Who needs it, when I drink I become the general…!!

-You'll land first…
-What if my parachute won't open?

-Helplo! Sergent Petrov! Operation “Sober Driver”
-It looks like your operation failed…!

Writing on the book: “Novel ‘Love’ volume I”

-And you really want us to find your wife?!

-Is it really you Yorick?

-This computer will do 50% of your work!
-Really?! Then configure two…!

-I'm not asking why is it raining, I'm asking: "Why there are puddles on the street"?

-Aladdin, judging by how you rub the magic lamp you don't have a woman…!

-The water is cold and I already have a medal for rescuing people from drowning…

-This is such a gorgeous dacha (summer cottage)! For such dacha it's not a shame to serve five years in prison…

-Beautiful Dnepr looks after a third bottle, even if it's the Moscow river…

-Citizen, where are you going at three o'clock at night?
-I'm going to listen to a lecture about how bad drinking is, read by my wife and mother-in-law…!!

-How is life, neighbor?
-I don't have a life; I have a fate!

-Do you have night life in your city?
-I do, but she is visiting her mama in the village…

-You need to close the door after you…!

-Vasilvanich, what will happen if you drink a lot of vodka?
-The day after tomorrow will happen...

-When will you finally decide: are you buying the table or not?

-Dear God, I haven't drink three days, send me a sip of water! I don't understand, why do you keep throwing me shovels…?

-Well, you could give vodka…

-Do you think that you're smarter than everyone?

Book title: "Kamasutra" -Life wasted in vein…

-Cut everywhere… Straighten up the ears… And remove the furriness.

-Who cares that he has two college degrees...
-I have five high school ones...

-Listen, how did you train cupid to hunt so well...?

-This is my son!!
-First pay the alimony, then point fingers!

-Understand, when you're talking to me you're talking to your paycheck…

-Are you the sexual majority or minority?
-I'm sexual loneliness…

-Nothing… I don't see anything… You will pay the penalty for custom service mockery!

-You're driving on the left side of the road, Sir!
-Why are you calling me “Sir”?

-Bless you…! And now we will announce the death sentence…

-Don’t worry, I’m tied up…!!

-Son, grandma will be very happy for our meeting…!

-I met a girl, but her parents were against my happiness, - they want me to marry her…

-It's Thursday outside and I don't want to work just as much as Friday…

-Hey pretty boy, I have a great offer, sell your soul…
-Lucifer, my offer is better, why don't you rent it!

Writing on the sign: "Recycle station"
-Do you accept whisky bottles?
-No Sir!

-Life starts after fifty…!
-Then let's drink 50 more grams…

-Instead of first aid I have a nurse!

-Doctor, I'll double my payment, just don't hit my leg…

CONCLUSION

Our passion is to spread the knowledge of the mysterious Russian language. We created educational and entertaining materials for learning Russian. You can find our educational materials in both printed and digital format on our website, on Amazon, Amazon Kindle, Apple Books, Barnes and Nobles, and Google play books. Be sure to visit our website for more information!

Our Website	https://foxitdimensions.com/
FoxIT Russian Alphabet Cards	https://foxitdimensions.com/russian-alphabet-cards.html
FoxIT Russian Alphabet Poster	https://foxitdimensions.com/russian-alphabet-poster.html
FoxIT Russian Alphabet Book	https://foxitdimensions.com/russian-alphabet-book.html

Daily Humor in Russian Life Series	https://foxitdimensions.com/russian-humor-books.html
Volume 1 - Mix	https://foxitdimensions.com/daily-humor-in-russian-life-volume-1.html
Volume 2 - Mix	https://foxitdimensions.com/daily-humor-in-russian-life-volume-2.html
Volume 3 - Alcohol Edition	https://foxitdimensions.com/daily-humor-in-russian-life-volume-3.html
Volume 4 - Rated “R” edition	https://foxitdimensions.com/daily-humor-in-russian-life-volume-4.html
Volume 5 - Beware of doctors	https://foxitdimensions.com/daily-humor-in-russian-life-volume-5.html
Volume 6 - Our Smaller Brothers	https://foxitdimensions.com/daily-humor-in-russian-life-volume-6.html
Volume 7 - Watch Out Children	https://foxitdimensions.com/daily-humor-in-russian-life-volume-7.html
Volume 8 - Love and Marriage	https://foxitdimensions.com/daily-humor-in-russian-life-volume-8.html
Volume 9 - Woman’s Touch	https://foxitdimensions.com/daily-humor-in-russian-life-volume-9.html
Volume 10 - Man’s Power	https://foxitdimensions.com/daily-humor-in-russian-life-volume-10.html
Volume 11 - Eat and Drink	https://foxitdimensions.com/daily-humor-in-russian-life-volume-11.html
Volume 12 - Man vs Woman	https://foxitdimensions.com/daily-humor-in-russian-life-volume-12.html
Volume 13 - Mix	https://foxitdimensions.com/daily-humor-in-russian-life-volume-13.html
Volume 14 - Mix	https://foxitdimensions.com/daily-humor-in-russian-life-volume-14.html

ЗАКЛЮЧЕНИЕ

Наша миссия - это распространять знание таинственного русского языка. Мы создали учебные и занимательные материалы для изучения русского языка. Вы можете приобрести их в книжном или электронном формате на нашем сайте, на Амазоне, на сайте книжного магазина Barnes and Noble, в книжных магазинах Google (EBooks) и Apple (IBooks). Читайте подробности на нашем сайте.

Наш сайт	https://foxitdimensions.com/
Русские Алфавитные Карточки	https://foxitdimensions.com/russian-alphabet-cards.html
Постер с Русским Алфавитом	https://foxitdimensions.com/russian-alphabet-poster.html
Книга Русский Алфавит	https://foxitdimensions.com/russian-alphabet-book.html

Ежедневный Юмор в Русской Жизни	https://foxitdimensions.com/russian-humor-books.html
Том 1 - Ассорти	https://foxitdimensions.com/daily-humor-in-russian-life-volume-1.html
Том 2 - Ассорти	https://foxitdimensions.com/daily-humor-in-russian-life-volume-2.html
Том 3 - Алкогольное Издание	https://foxitdimensions.com/daily-humor-in-russian-life-volume-3.html
Том 4 - Издание с рейтингом «16+»	https://foxitdimensions.com/daily-humor-in-russian-life-volume-4.html
Том 5 - Берегитесь врачей	https://foxitdimensions.com/daily-humor-in-russian-life-volume-5.html
Том 6 - Братья Наши Меньшие	https://foxitdimensions.com/daily-humor-in-russian-life-volume-6.html
Том 7 - Осторожно Дети	https://foxitdimensions.com/daily-humor-in-russian-life-volume-7.html
Том 8 - Любовь и Женитьба	https://foxitdimensions.com/daily-humor-in-russian-life-volume-8.html
Том 9 - Прикосновение Женщины	https://foxitdimensions.com/daily-humor-in-russian-life-volume-9.html
Том 10 - Мужская Сила	https://foxitdimensions.com/daily-humor-in-russian-life-volume-10.html
Том 11 - Ешь и Закусывай	https://foxitdimensions.com/daily-humor-in-russian-life-volume-11.html
Том 12 - Мужчина против женщины	https://foxitdimensions.com/daily-humor-in-russian-life-volume-12.html
Том 13 - Ассорти	https://foxitdimensions.com/daily-humor-in-russian-life-volume-13.html
Том 14 - Ассорти	https://foxitdimensions.com/daily-humor-in-russian-life-volume-14.html

Printed in Great Britain
by Amazon

39256457R00034